Judaica
PRESS

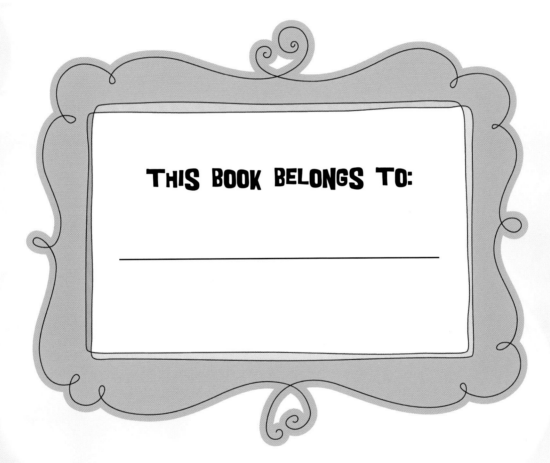

THIS BOOK BELONGS TO:

Wally the Worm Learns About KOSHER

By Rochel Burstyn

Judaica
PRESS

Dedicated to my wonderful Bubby Mrs. Nina Welis,
who, with Hashem's help, continues to grow the
most incredible garden and a beautiful family.
"Bardzo cie kocham!" (I love you!)

Wally the Worm Learns About Kosher

ISBN: 978-1-60763-229-0

Editor: Nachum Shapiro
Proofreader: Hadassa Goldsmith
Cover and internal illustrations: Evgeniy Ognarov

Judaica PRESS

THE JUDAICA PRESS, INC.
123 Ditmas Avenue / Brooklyn, NY 11218
718-972-6200 / 800-972-6201
info@judaicapress.com
judaicapress.com

Manufactured in the United States of America

"What's that?" Wally thought.
"It's so big and so green ...
The most beautiful leaf ball
That I've ever seen!"

He wiggled inside
His newly found treasure,
Took a bite of a leaf
And sighed with great pleasure.

"It's delicious! Fantastic!
Yummy and ... WOW!
I'm making my new home
Right here and right now!"

4

And that's what he did.
Wally moved in that day,
And zigzagged through the leaves
In every which way.

Day by day Wally grew
From his munching and chewing,
Unaware that in his future
Trouble was brewing ....

One day, a voice said, "Look!"
Stopping Wally mid-munch
In the yummy leaf meal
He was having for lunch.

The lettuce is ready!
What a beautiful sight!
We can make a fresh salad
For our dinner tonight.

Mindy lifted the lettuce head
With Wally still inside.
He was shaking with fear
And trying to hide.

8

Wally peeked through the leaves
And saw the backyard, now shrunk,
As Mindy stepped indoors
And put him down with a clunk.

Mindy's mother walked over
And admired the lettuce,
Saying, "How big a salad
Do you think this will get us?"

"Let's find out!" said Mindy.
"Let's toss it in!"
But Mommy said,
 "We must check it
Before we bite in."

"Uh-oh," thought Wally.
"What's this about biting?
And checking, and tossing?
This does NOT sound exciting!"

As the top leaf came off,
Wally shivered with fright.
Mindy's mommy washed it well
And held it up to the light.

"We check for worms and bugs,
No matter how small,
Because creepy crawlies
Are not kosher at all!"

"Can I help?" Mindy asked
As she pulled off another.
She washed and inspected it,
Just like her mother.

Mindy's mother checked hers over.
They stood, washing and looking
At the leaves for the salad
While dinner was cooking.

Then Wally's leaf was removed,
And although he felt shy,
He smiled through the light,
Waved, and said, "Hi ..."

A-A-AH-H!!!

Mindy screamed,
And before she could think,
She dropped Wally and his leaf
Right into the sink!

15

Her family came running
From all over the house.

Are you okay?

What happened?

Did you see a mouse?

Mindy yelled as she pointed,
"Look! A worm! It's true!"

"That's all?" said her sister.
"Why, he's more scared of you!"

16

Her mother said, "Eeww!
Oh, I'd also yell ...
I don't like creepy crawlies.
They bug me, as well.

"Good job finding it, Mindy!
Now, let's wash away
That yucky green worm,
That small stowaway!"

17

As poor Wally watched
The tap water trickle,
He cried: "Help me, Hashem,
I'm in quite a pickle!"

18

Then six-year-old Dov Ber
jumped up and cried, "WAIT!
Amazing! A worm!
That's really great!"

"I have a small jar
And I've wanted a pet!
Can I have this worm, Mom?
Please, do you let?
He doesn't need shots.
He won't bark or whine ..."

"As long as he stays in the jar,"
Mommy said, "then it's fine."

Then Wally the Worm
Sighed with relief
As Dov Ber picked him up,
Still on his leaf.

He put him in the jar
And poked holes through the top
As Mindy helped finish the salad
With a quick chop-chop-chop.

22

These days, Wally sits
On top of a shelf,
Munching his leaves
And smiling to himself.

And he watches the Kleins -
Including Mindy and Dov Ber -
Washing and checking,
Keeping KOSHER with care!

23

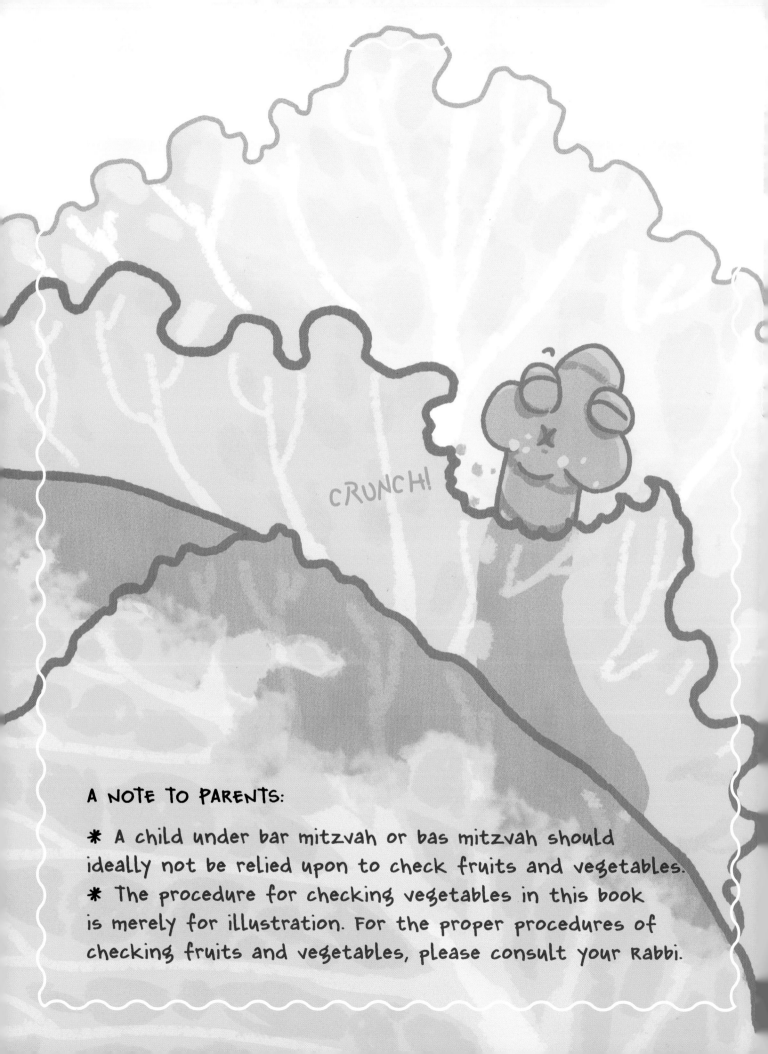

CRUNCH!

A NOTE TO PARENTS:

✳ A child under bar mitzvah or bas mitzvah should ideally not be relied upon to check fruits and vegetables.

✳ The procedure for checking vegetables in this book is merely for illustration. For the proper procedures of checking fruits and vegetables, please consult your Rabbi.

MORE JUDAICA PRESS BOOKS

How Mitzvah Giraffe Got His Long, Long Neck
By David Sokoloff

Rachel Golan   Rivka Landa
3-Minute Middos Stories for Children (and Parents, Too!)
Illustrated by Rona Weiss

MORE! 3-Minute Middos Stories for Children
Rachel Golan
Illustrated by Devorah Benedict

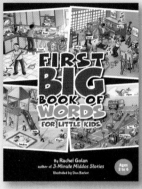

FIRST BIG BOOK OF WORDS FOR LITTLE KIDS
By Rachel Golan, author of 3-Minute Middos Stories
Illustrated by Dan Barlev
Ages 2 to 5

WHO WOULD HAVE GUESSED? IT'S ALL FOR THE BEST!
Written and illustrated by Loren Hodes

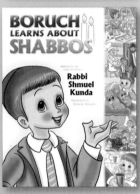

BORUCH LEARNS ABOUT SHABBOS
Adapted from an audio recording by Rabbi Shmuel Kunda
Illustrated by Devorah Benedict

BORUCH LEARNS ABOUT PESACH
By Rabbi Shmuel Kunda

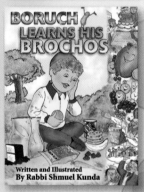

BORUCH LEARNS HIS BROCHOS
Written and Illustrated By Rabbi Shmuel Kunda

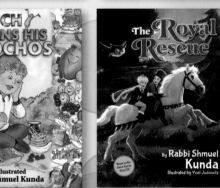

The Royal Rescue
By Rabbi Shmuel Kunda
Illustrated by Yoel Judowitz

WHERE ARE MY SHOES?
BY ROCHEL BURSTYN
Illustrated by Yisroel Groman

Let's Appreciate EVERYONE!
Bracha Goetz, author of Let's Stay Safe! and Let's Stay Pure

Aliza in Mitzvahland
by BRACHA GOETZ
Illustrated by YISHIA SUVAL

LET'S STAY PURE
by Bracha Goetz
illustrated by Sara Fogel

MY VERY OWN MITZVAH HANDS
BRACHA GOETZ
ILLUSTRATED BY MALKA WOLF

MY VERY OWN MITZVAH FEET
BRACHA GOETZ
ILLUSTRATED BY MALKA WOLF

The perfect introduction to Tefillah for kids!
I Daven Every Day
by Naomi Shulman

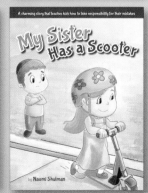

A charming story that teaches kids how to take responsibility for their mistakes
My Sister Has a Scooter
by Naomi Shulman

Let's Tell the Story of The Beis Hamikdash
A child's first introduction to Tisha B'Av
By Sara Blau

PHARAOH AND THE FABULOUS FROG INVASION
Written and illustrated by Osher Worsor